Stegosaurus
The thoughtful surprise

Written by Catherine Veitch

Illustrated by Barbara Bakos

MILES KELLY

There was once a Stegosaurus called Sonny, who lived with his family near a swamp.

The family used to live deep in the forest, but a mean Torvosaurus **chased them** from their cave.

Sonny tried not to **make a fuss** about moving to a new cave, but he **missed** his old home.

Sonny was often so lost in his own thoughts, he didn't look where he was going.

"Be careful!" shouted an angry Compsognathus, as Sonny almost flattened him.

And Sonny would forget
what he was told so often
his family thought his ears
were **stuffed with moss.**

"Remember, don't eat
the..." said Sonny's dad.

"Ee... urgh!" spluttered Sonny. "I forgot that moss tastes bitter!"

One night Dad said, "What **IS** it that keeps your mind so busy?"

It took a while for Sonny to find the right words.

"I think about LOTS of things," Sonny replied. "Mostly I think about our old home."

"I think about being chased away from our cave. And I think about my old friends," he said. "It makes me sad."

Sonny's dad thought about what his son had told him.

The next morning Dad said, "If you promise to be careful, why don't you visit your old friends?"

So Sonny **carefully headed back** towards his old home. He soon found his **friend** Ali, an Archaeopteryx.

They spent a lovely morning **playing together**, but soon it was time to go back home.

As Sonny left, his **tail spikes** caught a few of Ali's colourful **feathers**. They stuck to Sonny's tail.

But the friends didn't **notice** as they said goodbye.

Sonny was tired but **happy** when he got back to the cave.

"You can go out again tomorrow as long as you're careful," said Dad, picking the feathers off Sonny's tail.

The next day, Sonny ambled back through the forest and found his friend Alina, an Apatosaurus.

Alina was just about to eat, so they shared some juicy fern leaves together.

As Sonny turned to go, he brushed past some more ferns and a few stuck to his back plates.

But the friends didn't notice as they said goodbye.

Each time Sonny went out for the day, he came back to the cave a little happier.

"This cave almost feels like home now," said Sonny, as he wandered in to settle down for the night.

The next day Sonny **walked down** to the seashore to visit his friend Jag, a Juravenator.

At the beach, they dug some huge holes and found some **shiny shells.**

As Sonny turned to go, his tail **swished the shells**. Some flew into the air and landed between Sonny's back plates.

But the friends didn't **notice** as they said goodbye.

But when Sonny got back to the cave, his dad wouldn't let him in.

"It's a surprise!" said Dad picking shells off his son. "Give me a few minutes."

BANG!
SCRAPE!
CRASH!
came from inside the cave. What was Dad up to?

Sonny tried to imagine what his dad might be making... a dinosaur time machine; a giant forest funfair?

Moments later, Sonny and his sister stood in the middle of their cave with their mouths wide open.

Dad had used all the feathers, ferns and shells to decorate the cave.

"Every time you visited one of your friends, you came back with something stuck to you!" laughed Dad.

"Our cave looks amazing!" smiled Sonny. "I won't feel so sad now there's something from all of my old friends in my new home."